How to use this book

Follow the advice, in italics, given for you on each page.
***Praise** the children at every step!*

Detailed guidance is provided in the Read Write Inc. Phonics Handbook.

7 reading activities

Children:

- ☆ *Practise reading the speed sounds.*
- ☆ *Read the green and red words for the Ditty.*
- ☆ *Listen as you read the introduction.*
- ☆ *Read the Ditty.*
- ☆ *Re-read the Ditty and discuss the 'questions to talk about'.*
- ☆ *Re-read the Ditty with fluency and expression.*
- ☆ *Practise reading the speed words.*

Speed Sounds

Consonants

Say the pure sounds (do not add 'uh').

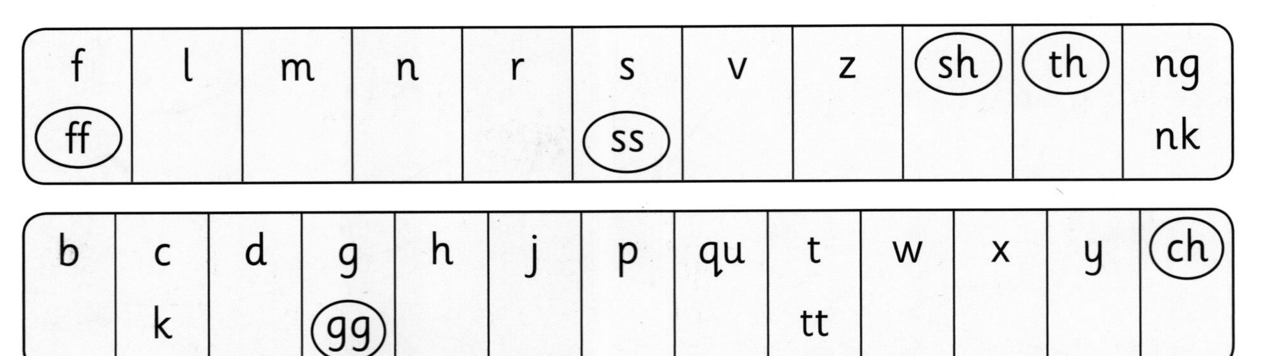

f	l	m	n	r	s	v	z	sh	th	ng
ff					ss					nk

b	c	d	g	h	j	p	qu	t	w	x	y	ch
	k		gg					tt				

Vowels

Say the sounds in and out of order.

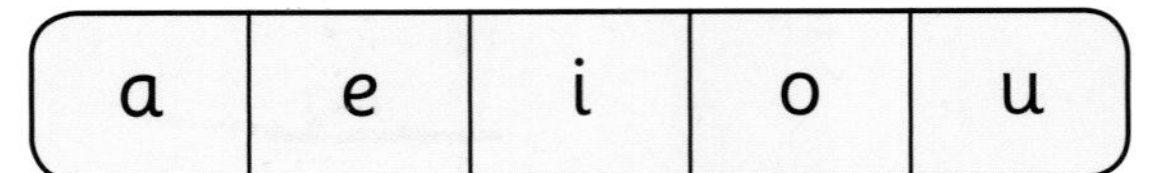

a	e	i	o	u

Each box contains only one sound. Focus sounds are circled.

Ditty 1 Let's swim

Green words

Read in Fred Talk (pure sounds).

swim get hot jump in

splash a drink

Read the root word first and then with the ending.

let → let's

Ditty 1 Let's swim

Introduction

In this story, two children go swimming. Let's see if they enjoy it!

let's jump in

let's swim

let's splash

brrrrrr

let's get a hot dri<u>nk</u>

Ditty 2

Egg and cress

Green words

Read in Fred Talk (pure sounds).

chop add yum and cut

an it egg on cress up

Read in syllables.

sand\`wich → sandwich

Red words

I put

Ditty 2

Egg and cress

Introduction

The girl in this story is making a sandwich. Let's see what she does.

I chop an egg and put it on

I add cress

I cut it up

yum yum

an egg and cress sandwich

Ditty 3 Stop the bus

Green words

Read in Fred Talk (pure sounds).

bus get six off on press
stop us

Read the root word first, then with the ending.

lot → lots

Read in syllables.

butt\`on → button

Red words

the of

Ditty 3 Stop the bus

Introduction

Do you like going on the bus? The girl in this story does!

get on the bus …

… six of us

press the button
stop the bus

get off the bus ...

... lots of us

Questions to talk about

Ditty 1

What do the children do in the swimming pool?

Why do they get out of the swimming pool?

What do you like doing in the swimming pool?

Ditty 2

What does the girl do first?

Does the girl enjoy her sandwich?

What is your favourite sandwich?

Ditty 3

How many people get on the bus?

How does the girl stop the bus?

Where do you like to sit when you go on a bus?

Speed words for Ditty 1

Children practise reading the words across the rows, down the columns and in and out of order clearly and quickly.

get	hot	drink	jump
swim	splash	in	a

Speed words for Ditty 2

chop	and	egg	put	it
add	cress	cut	up	on

Speed words for Ditty 3

bus	get	the	six	off
press	of	stop	us	on